Fall Leaves Fall!

by **ZOE HALL**

illustrated by
SHARI HALPERN

SCHOLASTIC INC.

New York · Toronto · London · Auckland · Sydney
Mexico City · New Delhi · Hong Kong · Buenos Aires

For Lauren

ISBN 0-439-32173-5

12 11 10 9 8 7 6   2 3 4 5 6/0

Printed in the U.S.A.   14

First Scholastic paperback printing, September 2001

The type was set in 25.5 point Worchester Medium.
The artist used painted and found papers to create collage illustrations for this book.
Book design by Kristina Albertson

All year long, my brother and I
wait for our favorite season to come.
Can you guess what it is?

Fall!

How do we know when fall is coming?

We watch the leaves.
In summer, the leaves on the trees are green.

When the leaves change color,
we know fall is here.

Look at all the fall colors!
Leaves turn red, orange, and yellow.

When the wind blows,
leaves start to fall from the trees.

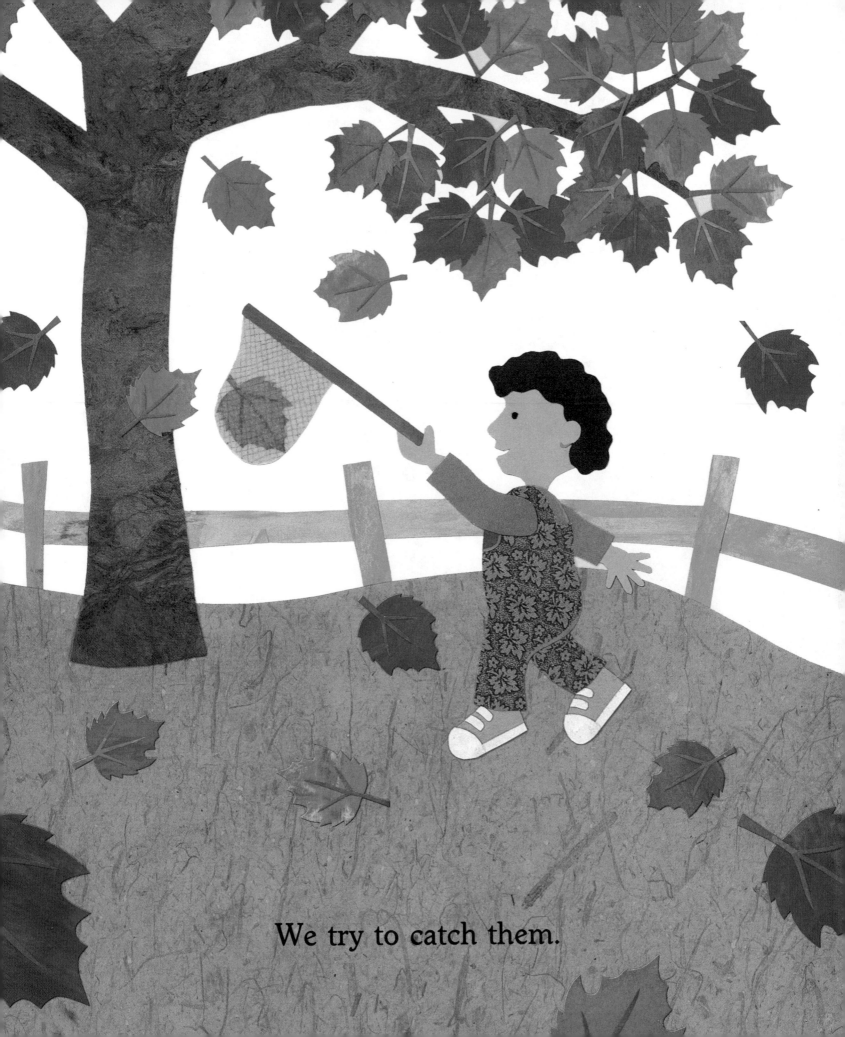

We try to catch them.

We like to stomp on the leaves — *CRUNCH!*
We like to kick the leaves, too.
All the fall colors fly back into the air.

We like to collect leaves.
Some leaves are very small.
Some leaves are big!

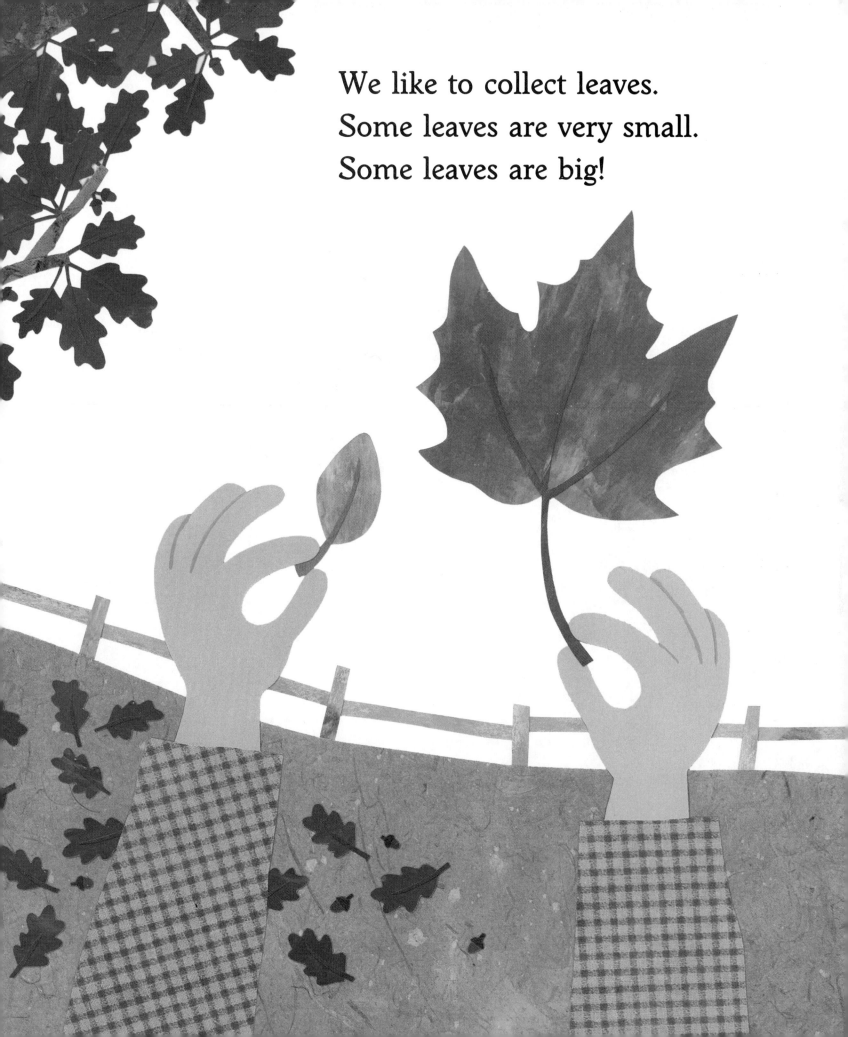

Some leaves have pointy edges.

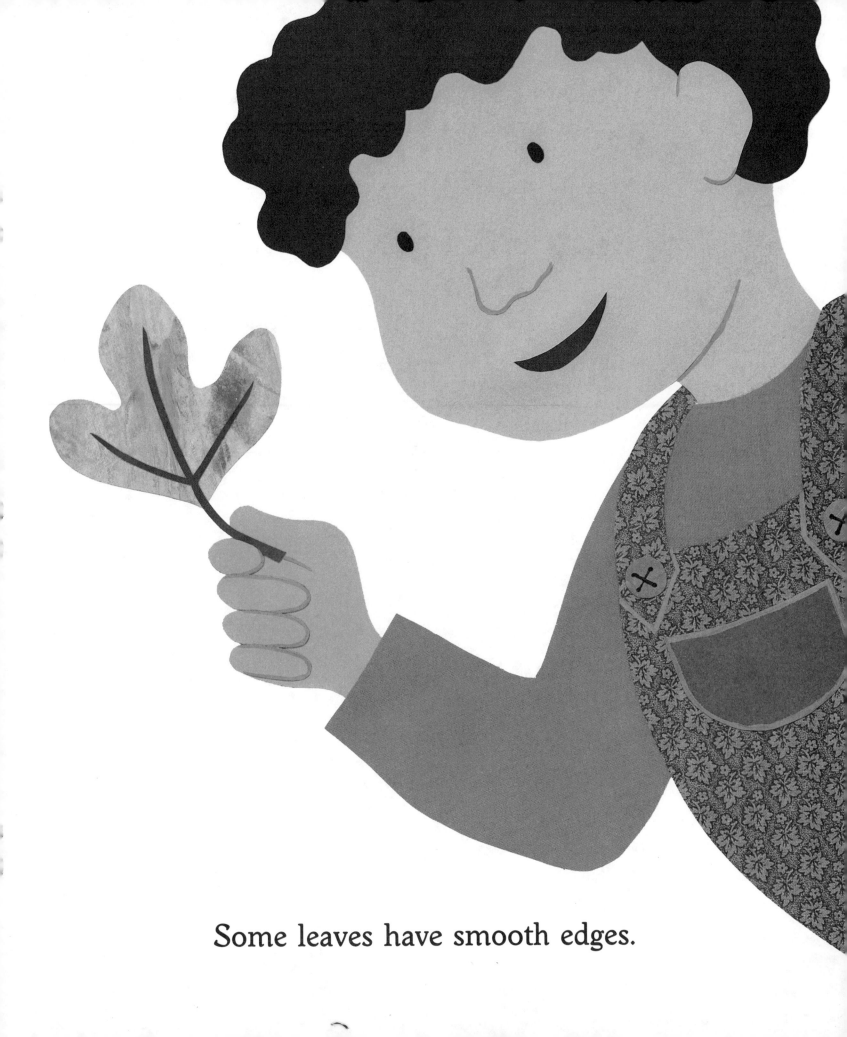

Some leaves have smooth edges.

When the leaves cover the ground,
it's time to rake them up.

At last, we have made a HUGE pile.
Next, . . .

. . . we jump in!

Inside, we drink mugs of warm cider and eat lots of cookies.

maple

sassafras

oak

These leaves came from our favorite trees.

We make pictures with our leaves.

Before long,
the leaves have turned brown
and the branches are bare.

All the fall colors are gone.
But we know they will be
back next year!

How leaves grow through the year:

1. In spring, small buds on tree branches open and tiny, light-green leaves appear. They grow bigger every day.

2. By summer, the leaves have grown to full size and are deep green. The leaves use sunlight to make food for the tree.

3. In fall, the green color fades and bright fall colors appear. The leaf stems weaken, and the leaves fall off the branches.

4. In winter, all of the leaves have fallen off. The tree makes buds, which will become new leaves in the spring.

Some leaves, such as needles on pine trees,
do not change color and do not fall off in fall.
Which fall colors do you see where you live?